DING
DONG
BELL

DING DONG BELL

Pussy's in the well

by Berta and

Elmer Hader

The Macmillan Company

New York   1957

Affectionately dedicated
to little Lem
and his mother
and grandmother

DING DONG BELL

"Meaow." A handsome, striped cat stood before the kitchen door of a shingle cottage that nestled in a clearing on a wooded hillside. Over the tree tops one could see the waters of a broad river. The last rays of the setting sun still warmed the far distant shore. The end of day was near and it marked the passing of another summer.

"Meaow," the cat said again. He scratched the door and stared at the door knob above, waiting for it to move as the door was opened. But no one answered his call. He moved slowly away, stopping every few steps to look back at the door. Then he walked around the corner of the house.

A flock of sparrows feeding on the ground took flight. They sought shelter in the thick growth of ivy that covered the brick chimney on the north end of the cottage. The cat paid no attention to the sparrows, nor to the bluejay screaming warnings from a nearby oak. He continued his slow walk. He looked at the boarded-up windows and the padlocked doors but he did not know that the cottage was closed and empty. The people who had rented the place for the summer had returned to their home in the city. They had no further use for the stray cat that had appeared at the kitchen door one morning. They had given him scraps of food left over from breakfast and he had found himself a sheltered place under the porch. Because of his handsome, striped coat they had named him Tiger. Tiger kept the field mice

8

away from the house and was given a bowl of milk from time to time as a reward.

Tiger was a friendly cat and it wasn't long before he was allowed to share the living room. The summer people were the only family he had ever known and he thought he belonged to them.

He was hunting mice in the woods on the day the summer people packed up and left. Day after day, Tiger waited patiently for his family to come back. When it rained, he hid under the porch. There were other cottages on the hill but they too, were closed. No one came to the wooded hillside now and Tiger was very lonely.

The days grew shorter and colder and one morning the grass on the hill was white with frost. The leaves on the trees about the cottage turned scarlet, yellow and brown. Chill winds from the north shook the trees and soon the ground on the hillside was covered with a carpet of many colors. Tiger stayed around the cottage still hoping his friends would return. But the cottage remained closed and silent.

As the fall days passed, many trees lost all their leaves. Through the bare branches Tiger could see the train that huffed and puffed up the side hill grade on its way to the city and whistled at the crossing when it returned in the evening. He could see too, the roof tops of houses in the village that lay at the foot of the hill. People lived in those houses for he could see smoke rising from chimney tops. Tiger determined to find himself a new home in the village.

Early one morning he followed the footpath down the hill. It was now overgrown with weeds. He passed a small orchard and the last of the summer cottages. He stopped to look and listen when he came to the railroad track. He hurried across. Now, he was in the village.

Though the sun was well up in a clear blue sky, it was still early and few people or moving cars were about. The garage and gas station had not opened for the day's business. Tiger stared at the buildings that rose from the sidewalks ahead. This was a new world to him.

Tiger walked past the garden and feed store, the coal and lumber yard and the post-office. Then he came to the main street of the village. It was lined with shop after shop.

12

A black and white cat stared at him from behind the window pane of a large grocery store. Some of the shops were opening their doors and he saw more early risers on their way to work. No one noticed the strange cat.

Tiger walked past the hardware store, the drugstore, the candy shop, the moving picture theater and the village tailor. They were closed. He was chased out of the barber shop and the laundry, and a bulldog growled from behind the door of Tony the cobbler. A policeman looked out from the door of the station house but he didn't see Tiger.

Tiger hurried past the firehouse at the far end of the street of shops. The loud honk of a milk truck horn scared him as he crossed the street and he didn't stop running until he was well past the village tavern.

The bell in the steeple of the little white village church tolled softly just as Tiger came to a street of many homes. Tall elms and great oaks grew near the curb. The wide street was divided by a strip of green lawn. Tiger purred as he moved along the pretty street. Surely he would find a home here.

14

He turned up a graveled driveway that led to a very big house. The milkman was just leaving and bottles of milk and cream stood in a row by the service entrance. "Meaow," said Tiger. This big house would be a wonderful home for a cat. He waited near the milk bottles until the door opened. "Meaow," he said hopefully. But the cook in the big house did NOT like cats. "GET OUT OF HERE," she cried. She reached for her broom and Tiger ran back to the street.

People from nearby houses hurried by on their way to the railroad station or to market. No one paid any attention to Tiger's friendly purring. He walked close to the hedge until he came to the entrance to the next house. It was the home of the village bank president. But the banker's gardener did not like cats. Neither did the banker's big dog!

Tiger stopped at house after house. Unfriendly cats lived in some and he was chased from others by barking dogs. Nowhere was there a place for a homeless cat. Footsore and weary, Tiger reached the end of the pretty street of homes. Only pine woods lay beyond.

The last house on the street was small. It needed painting and some shingles were missing from the roof. A few roses and chrysanthemums bloomed in the garden and the lawn was neat and tidy. There was a bottle of milk on the front porch. Just then the door

opened and a little girl and a little boy appeared. They laughed merrily as heads bumped when they both stooped to pick up the bottle of milk. Tiger purred softly. He liked this little house.

"Meaow," said Tiger. He rubbed his arched back against the picket fence and purred loudly. The children looked up and saw him.

"Here kitty—kitty," they called. Tiger trotted through the open gate with tail held high. He purred softly when the little girl picked him up and carried him into the house. "Look at the beautiful cat, mama," she said. "I wonder whose kitty he is. He looks lost. Can we keep him?"

The children lived in the little house with their widowed mother. She worked hard to keep her family together with the little money she earned. Another mouth to feed was a problem to be considered. Nevertheless, they welcomed the stray cat. The boy brought a box from the woodshed and put it behind the kitchen stove as a bed for the cat. The little girl lined it with some clean rags and old stockings. On their way home from school the next day, the children stopped at the library to look in the Lost and Found column of the village paper. They were happy that no one had advertised for a lost cat.

Tiger liked his new home. He kept the field mice out of the pantry and the wood rats out of the yard. He never bothered the birds that came to eat the crumbs the children scattered for them on the porch. He liked company and often followed the children part of the

way to school, or when they went on an errand for their mother.

One morning when the children and their mother set out for the village market, Tiger walked with them for a short way, then came back to his favorite spot on the front porch of the little house. He closed his eyes for a nap in the sun and purred contentedly. A deep growl brought him out of his dreams. A big black dog was coming across the lawn. Tiger was scared. Every hair on his body stood on end.

He leaped from the porch and ran for his life. The dog took after him. Tiger ran toward the thick underbrush at the edge of the woods. The dog was close behind and gaining with every leap. Luckily Tiger reached the low lying brush and scrambled under the blackberry brambles where the big dog could not follow. And then suddenly the ground gave way beneath him and he dropped from sight! Tiger had fallen through the rotten board cover of an old well.

Tiger landed on his feet at the bottom of the well. His claws sank deep into some paper. Luckily for Tiger, the well was dry and had been so for many years. Bits of the rotted board that covered the well top fell be-

side him. Tiger was scared more than ever. "Meaow,"
he howled. "Meaowwwwwwwwwww."

Only the big dog above heard him. He growled and
barked but he couldn't get through the sharp brambles
and brush and he didn't understand what had happened
to the cat. More boards fell into the well. Tiger
howled again and the dog barked furiously.

The children came home from the village ahead of
their mother. They heard the barking and hurried to
the edge of the woods. They recognized the dog. "It's
Butch," said the boy. "He's broken his rope again."

"GO HOME BUTCH," they both shouted.

Butch stopped barking. He knew the children and
saw that they were angry. He dropped his tail and
trotted away with a guilty look on his long face.

"Where's pussy?" said the little girl. "That mean ol'
Butch must have chased him and scared him to death."

21

"Here kitty-kitty," they both called. Tiger recognized their voices.

"Meaow," he answered. The children heard him. They parted the brush and saw the broken boards.

"Oh dear. He's in the well!" said the little girl. "How will we get him out?"

The boy ran to the shed. He soon returned with garden shears and a flashlight. He cut the brambles and they made their way to the well. They lifted part of the rotting board off the top and looked down the black hole with the flashlight. Tiger's eyes shone round and golden from below. "Meaow," he said.

"He's all right," said the boy. "We'll have to use the ladder to get him out. Good thing the well is dry." The children got the ladder and lowered it carefully into the well. The little boy climbed down. He was soon up again holding Tiger who was still clutching the papers he had fallen on at the bottom of the well. Tiger looked around for the dog. When he was satisfied that he was safe, he drew in his claws and the papers he had clung to unrolled. The children's eyes opened wide in surprise. Lying on the paper at their feet was something that looked like money—more money than they had ever seen before. They couldn't speak. They just stared.

"Meaow," said Tiger softly. The spell that held the children speechless was broken. They saw their mother coming through the garden gate.

"MAMA—MAMA," they shouted. "Come quick. The cat found money in the well. A lot of money. Hurry."

The children's mother placed her parcels on the porch and hurried to see what all the shouting was about. She stared at the money at her feet. She picked up a bill. It looked like real money but she had never seen thousand dollar bills before. Who did it belong to? It was not hers. How did it get in the well? For a moment she too, was speechless.

"If that is real money," she said, "we must find the owner." She picked up the newspaper the money was wrapped in to see if the owner of the money had written his name or address. The boy looked into the well but his flashlight showed only gravel, stones and bits of broken board. There was nothing to tell them who the money belonged to. The widow thought of all the things she could do with the money, and sighed.

"We must try to find the owner," she said to the children. "We'll take the money just as the cat found it, to the police station. Sergeant Jones will know what to do."

She carried the money in the paper into the house and tied it with a stout cord. Then the little family set out for the village police station. Tiger followed.

When the paper was opened on the sergeant's desk and he heard how the stray cat had found the money in the old well, Sergeant Jones' eyes almost popped out of his head.

"That's real money," he said. "That cat found a small fortune. You have done the right thing to bring it in. It isn't everyone who would have taken the trouble to find the owner." He studied the newspaper carefully. Then he wrapped the money up again, tied it securely and sealed it with wax. He walked across the room and put the package in the iron safe that stood in the corner. "I'll take it to the bank as soon as the police car comes around," he said. "It may take some time to find the owner. The first thing to do is to put an ad in the village paper. Most everyone reads the Lost and Found column and whoever put the money in the well, will surely call for it. You ought to get a fine reward. If no one claims the money . . . well, that

can be attended to later. In the meantime, 'Mum's the word.' " The sergeant looked at Tiger. "He's a handsome cat," he said. Tiger liked Sergeant Jones.

The widow followed Sergeant Jones' advice and put an ad in the paper. The children were so excited by the events of the day they had little appetite for supper. The next day Tiger walked to school with the children. They found it hard not to tell their schoolmates about the money the cat had found in the well, but they remembered Sergeant Jones had said "Mum's the word" and held their tongues.

Tiger walked on to the police station. "Good morning, Tiger," said Sergeant Jones. He liked cats. He lifted Tiger from the floor and set him on his desk. "I suppose you want to keep an eye on your money," he said with a chuckle. "Don't worry. It is safe in the bank."

The ad in the Lost and Found column of the village paper was read with great interest:

VALUABLE PACKAGE FOUND. ASK FOR SERGEANT JONES AT POLICE STATION.

In a short time townsfolk started coming to the station to claim the valuable package that had been found.

"If the valuable package is a purse," said one, "it's mine. I . . ."

"It is not a purse," interrupted Sergeant Jones. "Next."

"I lost a box of jewels," said another. "Where did you find it?"

"It is not a box of jewels," said the sergeant. "Next."

None of the villagers who came to the station had lost money. Then a stranger in town spoke up. "I lost a valuable package when I passed through here on a business trip," he said. "Is the package you found wrapped in something?"

"You should know," said Sergeant Jones. "If it is your package." He glanced at the village paper.

"My valuables," said the stranger, "were wrapped in a newspaper."

31

"What did you say was wrapped in a newspaper?" The stranger hesitated a moment. "Why-er-er, I wrapped up some money. Quite a lot of money," he said. "I needed a large amount of cash for a business deal that I was about to close. I stopped to eat a bite of lunch just outside the village. I sat down near a house at the edge of the woods. I always kept the package with me. After lunch I took a nap. Then I drove on. Unfortunately, I left my package behind. I soon discovered my loss and returned but I couldn't find the exact place where I had stopped. I had to continue west to finish my business and I just returned today. I was about to advertise my loss when I read that my package had been found. I'll reward the finder."

Tiger stared at the stranger and purred loudly. Sergeant Jones glanced at the calendar on the wall. "What was the paper and the date you wrapped the money in?" The stranger looked at the calendar.

"Why-er—the village paper er-er about a month ago."

"Sorry you lost your money," said Sergeant Jones. "The package that was found was not lost a month ago. Just leave your name and address and we will let you know if your money is found and turned in."

Days and weeks passed by. Tiger lived happily with his new family but he often visited his friend Sergeant Jones at the police station. None of the many people who called could identify the package Tiger had found in the well.

One day when Tiger walked into the station house, Sergeant Jones stood up. "I've been waiting for you, Tiger," he said. "It is time we got some advice from the judge about that money you found." Tiger followed the sergeant across the street to the office of Judge Andrews. He sat on the desk while the sergeant told the whole story.

"There is a very good law for just such a case," said the judge. "Most laws are full of whereas'es and wherefore's only understood by lawyers. In simple words,

Sergeant Jones, the law says FINDERS KEEPERS, LOSERS WEEPERS. Our friend Tiger found the money, so rightfully the money belongs to him. But a cat has no use for a roll of paper money. He can't eat it and it hasn't a pleasant smell like catnip. In this case the owner of the property has a claim too. Therefore, the money will be divided between the owner of the cat and the owner of the land on which the money was found. We know the owner of the property. Now we must find the owner of the cat."

The story of the cat who had found a fortune appeared on the front page of the village paper and in papers all over the country. Photographers took pictures for television and countless listeners heard the story over the radio. Many people now claimed the cat and the money.

In the little house at the edge of the woods, neither the children nor their mother knew that the stray cat they had taken in was now rich. They had no radio and seldom saw the village paper so they had not heard the news. On the day the news of Tiger's good fortune was broadcast, the pantry shelves were almost bare and the little family set out for the village market. Tiger was hunting in the woodshed and his family were well on their way before he missed them. But Tiger did not like being left alone, so he started for the village too.

Few people were on the street and no one paid any attention to Tiger until he came to the banker's house. The gardener saw him and ran to the garden gate. "Here-kitty-kitty," he called in sweet tones. The banker's dog must have heard the news for he just grinned and wagged a friendly tail. But Tiger remembered the shouting gardener and the barking dog. "Pfffssst," he hissed and ran along.

As Tiger passed the biggest house on the street, the kitchen door opened. The cook saw the cat who had found a fortune. The news of Tiger's luck had changed her feelings toward cats. Now, she loved them. "Here pussy-pussy," she called in honeyed tones. But Tiger had not forgotten his call at the big house nor the cook's broom. "Pfffsst," he said and hurried along.

The village innkeeper saw Tiger. "Oh-ho," he said. "There goes the lucky cat that found the money. If he's looking for an owner, I'm his man. I'll lock him in the wine cellar. Then the money he found will be mine." He ran after Tiger and scooped him up. Tiger was surprised. He did not like being handled roughly. "Pffssst," he hissed angrily and his sharp claws dug into the innkeeper's hands.

"OUCH!" yelled the innkeeper. He dropped Tiger and ran back to the Inn to wash his scratched and

bleeding hands. "That's not a CAT," he muttered. "That's the devil himself and he can keep his gold."

It was near the holidays and the village stores were crowded with shoppers. Tiger was scared by the crowds and he could not find his family. So he hurried home again.

For weeks Judge Andrews had listened patiently to many people who claimed to be the owner of the lucky cat. On the morning of the day the children and their

mother had walked into the village to shop, he had telephoned his decision to the editor of the village paper.

The children and their mother moved slowly around the big village market. Rows of chickens, geese and turkeys hung on the walls behind the counters of the busy butchers. Packages of meats and fish wrapped in cellophane filled ice-chilled shelves nearby. Boxes and trays of grapes, oranges and apples were placed in neat rows and the bins just below were full of turnips, onions and cabbages. Bags of potatoes were piled against the wall.

All over the store, the shelves in aisles and on walls, were filled with all kinds of food. There would be no roast turkey, or chicken or ham on the table in the little house at the edge of the woods. But they were thankful for what they had. They bought a few things and the last pennies in the purse were spent for a can of cat food.

As they left the market with their packages, they were stopped by Sergeant Jones. He held up a copy of the village paper. He pointed to the big black headlines. CAT WINS FORTUNE. "Haven't you heard the news?" he asked. "This is the story of your cat. Tiger is a rich cat. A lot of people claimed him but Judge Andrews knew that you took him in when he was just a poor stray and decided that you were the rightful owners. The judge also decided that, as owners of the property where the money was found, you were to share the cat's good fortune. The judge gave me some

legal papers for you to sign. Then you will be the cat's lawful owners and I can turn the money he found over to you."

The children and their mother stared at Sergeant Jones. They couldn't believe their ears. Just because they had been kind to a stray cat, all this good fortune had come to them. They crossed the street to the police station. After the papers were signed, Sergeant Jones gave them some money. "I am sure that lucky cat wants to treat his family to a holiday dinner," he said with a chuckle. "The rest of the money is in the bank in your name."

They all thanked the sergeant and the little family returned to the big market. This time, they bought plenty of food to fill all the pantry shelves in the little house near the woods. One shelf would have special tid-bits for Tiger. The children picked out a fine basket to put behind the stove and a soft blanket to line it with. They put their packages in a village taxicab and started for home.

Tiger was waiting on the porch. He ran across the lawn purring loudly. He purred when the pantry shelves were filled with good things to eat and he purred when his new basket was put behind the stove. But Tiger's purrs of happiness were not for the things that money can buy. Tiger's real fortune was a happy home and loving friends.

Hader Books

BIG CITY

THE BIG SNOW

COCK-A-DOODLE-DOO

DING DONG BELL

FARMER IN THE DELL

THE FRIENDLY PHOEBE

HOME ON THE RANGE

LITTLE APPALOOSA

THE LITTLE STONE HOUSE

LITTLE TOWN

LITTLE WHITE FOOT

LOST IN THE ZOO

THE MIGHTY HUNTER

PANCHO

RAINBOW'S END

THE RUNAWAYS

THE SKYROCKET

SPUNKY, A SHETLAND PONY

SQUIRRELY

WISH ON THE MOON